KATHLEEN

KATHLEEN

A Christian's Journey into Alzheimer's

Stanley Trickett

Terra Nova Publications

First published in Great Britain in 2006 by
Terra Nova Publications International Ltd
PO Box 2400, Bradford on Avon, Wiltshire BA15 2YN

Cover design by Roger Judd

ISBN 1 90194 948 6

Printed in Great Britain
by Bookmarque Ltd, Croydon

CONTENTS

PREFACE

For most human beings, whether they are people of faith or not, there has been a moment when they have reflected on the age-old questions: What is the purpose of my existence? Are there any certainties? Insignificant as I am, can I add to the quality of life by making a positive contribution to the peace of the world and the well-being of my neighbour?

These are enormous questions, but there appears to be common agreement in acknowledging that there are at least two certainties— that each one of us will die, and that each of us will suffer pain, both physical and emotional, at some stage in our life. Maybe this is a gloomy, pessimistic viewpoint, but for Christians grappling with the mystery of faith in their God, these are truths that form the very basis of that 'peace which passes all understanding'. There is the knowledge that light follows darkness, despair can be the gateway to hope, and death leads to new life in all its abundance.

It is not so easy to live in the light of such truth, though, particularly in times of change and suffering. The ancient Israelites believed that illness was a punishment for sin, often sin handed down from generation to generation. Jesus' disciples had been brought up in this belief, and so it was that as they walked along together, when they met a man who had been blind since birth, they realised what an ideal time this was to question Jesus: "Rabbi, who sinned, this man or his parents, that he was born blind?"

The answer was clear and concise. Neither the man nor his parents had sinned. The encounter took place so that God's works might be revealed in him. Then Jesus healed the man, and his sight was restored. Meeting Jesus, the man was healed at the point of his need, thus revealing to all around him the unconditional love that is given without us either deserving it or being worthy of it.

Many people have experienced the anxiety of waiting for a medical diagnosis, particularly when our dear ones are involved. For the relatives of patients facing test results for Alzheimer's disease, the waiting is particularly difficult. Kathleen, after her initial expression of pain and shock, remained calm and accepting throughout the ordeal, and when her family faced the confirmation of her illness, her concern was centred on them rather than on herself.

Here began an immense challenge —coping with day-to-day illness, planning for the future, and accepting that retirement as a longed-for time together was not going to be part of the future. It has been said that life is what happens to us while we are busy making other plans. Suddenly that became a reality.

1

THE DIAGNOSIS

I well remember the day when Kathleen was first told by her GP that he felt that she might well have Alzheimer's disease. I remember too her loud and vehement protests – "No, no, I've just got a bad memory, that's all!" She was clearly horrified by the thought that it could well be the beginning of Alzheimer's, knowing full well that the disease was terminal; that it took away the ability to live a normal life, and that the restrictions which came with it would change her life for ever.

Her reaction was quite understandable, since we all know that it is the short-term memory which is affected at first. People forget the information which they have just been given, or where they have placed something. In Kathleen's case, she would forget where she had promised to meet me, which could be quite alarming in the middle of a busy town. I shall never forget the day she failed to arrive back at the car and, going in search of her, I suddenly found her running down the middle of a busy street, a shopping bag in each hand, looking quite panic-stricken, as she clearly had no idea which way to go.

From that day onwards I was determined that I would not let her out of my sight but, careful though I was, I was not careful enough. The next scare came when I decided to take her, with friends, to the open-air concert and firework display at Wilton House. Kathleen loved it. We all did. But it was at the end, when we were packing up our picnic things – thousands around us were doing the same, and it was dark – that I turned to take hold of Kathleen's hand and discovered that she was no longer there!

She had seen crowds milling in one direction – towards the wrong car park, as it happens – and she had joined them! I did not know which way she had gone, but I did know that between us and the car park, to which she might well have been heading, was an unfenced river. The danger was obvious. It was I who panicked this time, running to the nearest security tent and pouring out my worst fears.

The security officer I spoke to could not have been kinder. To my amazement, instead of encouraging me to carry on with my search, he made me sit down in a corner of the tent, and assured me that "our men will find her". What I did not know was that there were dozens of security officers around the enormous park, and that they were all in touch with each other by field telephone. Kathleen's description was quickly circulated, and in what seemed like no time at all the message came through: "We have found her, and are on our way up to you now."

The relief on my part was indescribable, and I could not thank those men enough for what they had done. Kathleen had indeed gone to the wrong car park, and was just standing at the entrance waiting for us when she was recognised by one of the attendants, who immediately took charge of her and brought her back to us.

She herself was quite oblivious to the concern she had caused, and just rejoined us as though nothing had happened!

But what a wonderful God our God is! He must have known that this was precisely the kind of experience which I was going to need in caring for Kathleen, who herself had now succumbed to dementia. He must have known how valuable that experience would be in helping me to understand just a little of what Kathleen was now going through, and in getting alongside others with the disease.

I never found myself blaming God for Kathleen's condition, but I often found myself asking: Why does it have to be like this? And why are we not being allowed to enjoy a healthy and active retirement, with lots of tennis, swimming, long walks in the countryside and lazy afternoons on the beach? Why had the leading of church worship – which I had always enjoyed – and the leading of discussion groups, now become so exhausting? Was it because I was getting old? True, I was past my three score years and ten, but I felt quite strongly that God still had work for me to do.

I eventually concluded that whilst the leading of worship and groups was good for my ego, it was my wife who now deserved my time and attention. After all, she had loved and cared for me all those years. Was it too much to ask that I should now give her all the care and time that I could? After all, there were others who could lead worship and groups. But there were very few who would be prepared to spend time with someone who had dementia. The caring church was indeed caring —but only up to a point.

One very caring church had been the last parish where we had ministered together, from which I had retired. When she was diagnosed with Alzheimer's Kathleen had written a letter for publication in our parish magazine. Her faith, her care for others and the courage with which she faced what lay ahead shines through, and it is reproduced here:

11

Dear Friends,

I always remember hearing about a man who had been to his doctor, and at the end of the examination the doctor saying to him, "I wish I could tell you that you had cancer – cancers can often be cured – but I am afraid that what you have is Alzheimer's disease, for which there is no known cure."

Those words came back to me when, some time later, I too received the same diagnosis following a number of tests at Southampton General Hospital. "There are," I was told, "one or two rare forms of this disease which do respond to treatment, but unfortunately yours is not one of them." I could not believe what I was hearing. I had always been so fit and well, mentally as well as physically. This surely could not be happening to me.

True, my memory was failing a little – and, yes, I did sometimes get confused – particularly when under pressure. But I knew enough about Alzheimer's disease to know that there was much more to it than just that —that it was a steady down hill route; that it could only get worse, and that it was terminal.

When I eventually confided in my family, they were shocked – but wonderfully supportive – as have been all our friends and parishioners as the news of my condition became generally known. Part of the object of writing this article whilst I can still be reasonably coherent is to let you know how much your understanding and support means to me.

I do not write in order to gain sympathy, but so that if any of you or your loved ones are unfortunate enough to contract this dreadful disease (and it does happen to younger as well as older people), then you will gain courage from what I have to tell you about my own experience.

After years spent in his service, has God let me down? Well, I can honestly say that my feelings for most of the time are feelings of thankfulness —not for the disease, but for the many wonderful things that have happened to me, for my family, for this community, for all the love and support I get back from within the church, and outside it.

Thankful, too, after the initial shock, for that special feeling of acceptance and peace as I came to terms with the fact that although there was no way back, God's promise that "I will never leave you nor forsake you" was real, and that already I was safe in his care. Not only that, but in response to the many prayers which have been offered for me, God has enabled me to live a fairly normal life for at least some of the time.

There are days when you will find me forgetful, a little confused, and sometimes a bit repetitive, and for all this I ask your forbearance.

Shopping can sometimes be a problem, and I have been known to forget where we have parked the car, or I had promised to meet Stanley. But, I am still able to enjoy a game of tennis, walks, outings, and holidays, and was recently able to support Stanley as he led a Christian holiday group to northern Italy.

I am therefore, with God's help, determined to do as much as I can for as long as I can. Retirement, when it comes next year, may not be quite as we had planned it, but there will be blessings —of that I am sure, and I know that the peace of God which means so much to me will not be taken from me.

Beginning the day with God is also very important to me – I am usually in church for morning prayer at 7.30 a.m. It is there, perhaps more than at any other time, that I feel the presence and peace of God which takes me forward into the new day.

Rarely, if ever, have I been tempted to cry out, 'Why, God, are you letting this happen to me?' All I know is that there is still some quality of life left for me, and that God wants me to make the most of every second.

Before we were married, Stanley and I came across these words, which meant a great deal to us and still do: 'Trust in the Lord with all your heart and lean not on your own understanding; in all your ways acknowledge him, and he will direct your path.'[1] I can only say that this has a greater significance for us now than it has ever done. And more than ever I know these words to be true!

October 1st 1966 was a very special and exciting day for me. It was the day of my husband's Ordination and I remember it well. It was also the day I began to share in his new and exciting ministry. Always, however, I have felt called to support him in quiet and non-public ways and this is the first time in our thirty years of ministry together that I have ever written anything for any of our parish magazines.

I do so now, while I still have the ability, because of Alzheimer's disease which is something about which there is all too little understanding and is a disease of which many people are understandably afraid. I do not look forward to the inevitable deterioration in my condition, but I do know that when Jesus said, "I will never leave you nor forsake you", that is true for me. And that is what carries me forward.

With my thanks again for your love, support and understanding.

Kathleen

[1] Prov. 3:5-6

2

BLESSINGS IN DISGUISE

The Millennium year 2000 was a year full of unexpected changes, many of which were unwelcome, but most of which turned out to be 'blessings in disguise'.

It was soon after we had moved into our retirement home that one morning, having been invited out to a house in the village for coffee, Kathleen and I returned home and, because there was some little time before lunch, decided that we would tackle a few jobs while we could. There were, for instance, all those boxes in the garage which needed to be stored in the loft overhead, and hadn't I thoughtfully had a loft ladder installed precisely for such situations as this?

So as Kathleen wandered around the house, uncertain about quite what she was expected to do but still basking in recollection of the sheer joy of a very happy coffee morning in the company of some delightful people who had all been extremely kind to her, I busied myself with the task of moving those boxes, which had been a bit of a nuisance for some time. The first task was to lower the extending ladder and make sure it was in precisely the right position. I had heard tales of accidents with extending ladders which either had not been fully extended or else had been left on a skew. I was not going to make that mistake myself.

One box at a time was enough, so I confidently took one up the ladder and slid it into the slot I had in mind when, without warning, the top end of the ladder pulled away from its moorings and, with me still on top, crashed down on to the concrete garage floor beneath. As I hit first one obstacle and then another, the excruciating pain in my back made me realise that I had severely damaged myself. And the one thing I remembered being told was that in circumstances such as these I must not move until there was professional help and advice.

To get such professional advice and help I needed a phone. But I could not move. And how could I get Kathleen to understand what I needed? I just had to try. I persuaded her to come into the garage. That was the easy part. She could see that something was wrong, but was not quite sure what had happened. So – after she had said a few times, "Oh dear," and, "What can I do?" – I asked her to pass me the telephone. This she did not understand, first of all passing me a hammer and then a screwdriver; she was trying very hard to be helpful, but because of her condition she was unable to focus on 'telephone'.

After many attempts I succeeded in getting her to pass me the cordless phone, so that I was able first of all to call for an ambulance, and, secondly, to contact Elizabeth, at whose home we had had coffee, to get much-needed help for Kathleen. The ambulance would almost certainly be taking me off to hospital —but Kathleen could not be left alone.

I was right about the ambulance and the hospital, and Elizabeth, who arrived about the same time, immediately assured me that she would take care of Kathleen and keep an eye on the house. What a friend!

At the hospital, after all the usual preliminaries, I was seen by a consultant who looked at me with a very serious expression on his face and said that, although I had not damaged my spinal cord, I had in fact crushed two vertebrae and would need to be kept in hospital for at least six to eight weeks. I was horrified. Who could I possibly get to look after Kathleen for all that time? Washing, dressing and personal care had already become quite difficult, and there were days when by evening I was quite exhausted. Yet I had promised myself that no way would Kathleen ever go into care. She had been a wonderful wife, and the least I could do was to care for her 'till death us do part'. But I was now in an impossible situation. There was no way that I could even begin to look after her in my present state.

Just when I was despairing of finding a solution, on to the scene came another angel in disguise, in the form of Sue McCauley, a community psychiatric nurse who was the kindest, most competent and caring CPN that anyone could wish to meet. She immediately took charge of the situation, organised a bed for Kathleen in the Old Manor psychiatric hospital on a temporary basis, and then paid me a reassuring visit to let me know that Kathleen was in good hands, well looked after, and that I would be able to see her as soon as I was able to get up and about. I would then be able to take her back home with me if that was what we wished.

I was, in fact, only partly reassured. Yes, she was undoubtedly in good hands, but no one understood her needs in the way that I did, so I worried endlessly about how she would be reacting to her new carers and how she would settle in —however temporary the situation.

When I look back, I think that the staff on my ward were

just so patient with me, for I was constantly asking them for information about my wife, and asking them to find out whether they were quite sure that she was all right. That assurance was given over and over again, yet it was not enough. I needed to see her, and that was not possible. She could not get to me, and I was not allowed up for those six to eight weeks.

They were the longest weeks of my life! But eventually I was discharged, and Elizabeth took me over to the Old Manor hospital, where I would be meeting Kathleen after two whole months. Would she have changed? Would she still recognise me? How would she react after all this time? What would her stay in a psychiatric hospital have done to her?

We arrived at breakfast time, and Elizabeth waited outside in the corridor while a staff nurse ushered me into the nearly empty breakfast room and very tactfully led the few late breakfasters out into the nearby lounge. She then brought us a fresh pot of tea and left us alone together. The moment of truth had arrived. What would be Kathleen's reaction?

First there was a gentle grin; then a broad smile, followed by a look of sheer joy. We were there! We had made it! We were back together! If there was any surprise or puzzlement in Kathleen, it did not show. Her condition meant that conversation was well nigh impossible, so I did most of the talking while she responded with a beautiful smile and occasionally reaching out to touch my hand. It was heaven! It surpassed anything I had dared to hope for. The sun was shining and it was a beautiful morning so, hand in hand, we walked out into the grounds, passing close to where Elizabeth was sitting, partly concealed by a pillar, anxious not to be seen in case it spoiled things for Kathleen and me.

Most psychiatric hospitals seem to have a stigma which is difficult to shake off, and the Old Manor was no exception. It is not really surprising, then, that I feared the worst when Kathleen had been taken in there. I was certainly not prepared for what I found.

First of all there were no uniforms which, although making it harder for people like me to know just who was who, somehow just added to the relaxed and cheerful atmosphere amongst staff and patients alike.

Another surprise was the ease with which (with permission) we were allowed to take our loved ones out —or even home. Security was (thank goodness) fairly tight but, as one member of staff was heard to say, "This is not a prison, you know." Indeed it was not. In fact on 1st October they helped organise a celebration tea party for our wedding anniversary, which was preceded by a little service of Holy Communion, laid on by our parish priest, Michael, and his curate, Kim.

Friends and guests came in from our previous parishes and it was a most delightful afternoon, with champagne and a celebration cake, to say nothing of the speeches, and so on. Kathleen beamed throughout and responded in a lovely way as, one by one, the guests gathered around with their hugs and good wishes. She may not have fully understood what it was all about, but she knew that it was special.

I discovered that Kathleen's ward was an assessment unit, and that after a while she would be expected to move on, either to a nursing home, or back home to me. Realistically, I was beginning to see that the latter was not an option. I was going to need carers to look after me.

Never was I going to manage to care for my wife as well. But it was Sue McCauley who once again came up with an answer.

There was a vacancy, she said, at Glenside Manor Nursing Home, just a few miles outside Salisbury, and since Kathleen had very few assets of her own it could be funded by Social Services. I should have been overjoyed, but by now Kathleen was settled in and well cared for at the Old Manor, and I was not happy about the disruption of moving her to somewhere entirely new. In any case, I had been told on more than one occasion that most people went to Glenside Manor to die! So happy were we with the Old Manor that I objected to the move. But I was told that the hospital was for sick people requiring treatment, and Kathleen did not fall into that category. I do not like surprises, particularly when it involves moving into the unknown.

Instead of being cross with me, Sue was very gentle and said that whilst she fully understood what I was saying, perhaps I could at least go and have a look at Glenside Manor, then we could have another chat. This I agreed to do.

It was at times like this that I wished so much that I was able to discuss the matter with my dear wife. But no! The decision had to be mine. And so to Glenside I went, not knowing quite what to expect, but fearing that any move could be upsetting.

It was a lovely sunny afternoon when I swung the car into the drive of Glenside Manor, and I had to admit that from the outside it looked very attractive. The proprietor met me and explained the layout, what life was like for the residents, and the kind of care Kathleen could expect. He answered all my questions —and did so in such an honest and straightforward way that I had to admit that I was beginning to warm to the idea of Kathleen moving there.

What finally sold the idea to me was my introduction to Robert, the charge nurse on Kathleen's wing. Such a kind and sensitive person. He showed me one of the rooms and then answered the questions which even I had forgotten to ask! Nothing was too much trouble, either for Kathleen or her family, and I knew then that this really was the right place for her. This was confirmed as I witnessed that same care and patience and sensitivity in the rest of the staff. Kathleen would not just be cared for —she would be loved.

Robert told me that Kathleen would be sharing a room at first on the ground floor, but that her bed was next to the window and so she had a lovely outlook.

For meals there was a choice of menu, and getting-up and going-to-bed times were very much according to the patient's wishes. There seemed to be lots of staff, kindly and smiling and helpful, and there was a lovely feel about the whole place. Outside there were flower gardens and walks, with beautiful views across the valley. I wondered how anyone could object to living there.

Within a week Kathleen was offered a single *en suite* room on the first floor, with excellent views, and the added advantage of privacy when she had visitors, and the lift was just a few yards away. The decision was made. The transfer from the Old Manor did not appear to concern Kathleen at all. And Robert kept a very close eye on her throughout.

3

LOST —AND FOUND

Elizabeth Burdett, a friend, writes

Loss comes to us all in life, whether it be loss of a home or job, bereavement or a broken relationship. In a material world financial loss may mean the lack of status resulting in lost confidence, self-esteem, and many other 'selfs' that this modern society values so much.

The Christian life as a pilgrimage of discovery and commitment to love in its deepest sense speaks strongly about loss and rebirth or renewal. Strong words indeed, but needing great resources of courage and determination to meet the daily challenges. And to wait upon God as he reveals this great paradox of 'lost and found' as part of discipleship.

In the early days of Kathleen's diagnosis and illness those of her friends who were privileged to be at her side glimpsed a little of her personal suffering, and the pain being experienced by her husband and children. Despite growing confusion and forgetfulness, Kathleen continued her daily life of prayer and worship, welcoming with her usual cheerfulness the many people who, for so many reasons, came to the Vicarage seeking her guidance and support. As a very private person she spoke little about her illness, but we, her friends, were aware that the loss of such skills as playing the piano and driving the car; and of her independence when shopping, visiting the hairdresser, or attending parish meetings, were a sadness she alone could come to terms with.

So, too, with the support she needed to give her husband at the end of his ministry in a very busy parish. His love was her greatest comfort, and only those close to him will remember his words of pain and loss: "I don't know how I shall bear it or manage without her." Here, perhaps, was the greatest loss of all: that Stanley and Kathleen could no longer plan their retirement together, with all its hope of togetherness and shared pleasures. Their commitment became one of resting in God, facing an unknown future and a new life —secure in his love.

So what could possibly be the positives in this situation? Well, firstly there was a home to leave and another waiting to welcome them, and the finding within themselves a new ministry of standing aside from leadership and being just ordinary people with a problem. Time was needed for the acceptance of this drastic change in lifestyle, and time was something that retirement offered. With Stanley now released from so many time-consuming tasks, and able to care for Kathleen with such patience and devotion, Kathleen blossomed and enjoyed many simple pleasures in spite of her limitations.

They even managed short holidays together; they entertained their friends and spent precious time with their children and grandchildren. When Stanley had a serious accident, and serious decisions had to be made, Kathleen's love and trust in God were a shining example to all whose lives she touched. That was five years ago.

Today the signs of deterioration in her physical and mental health are visible, but serenity streams from her — in a smile, even an amused chuckle, in the songs she still sings, but above all in the radiant joy she experiences at regularly weekly worship with her husband.

So gradually, through loss, our Lord makes himself known to us, shares the burdens, and strengthens us for the days ahead. We recall his words to Nicodemus; his words to the rich man who wanted to follow him; and his words to his dear friends mourning the death of their brother. They all had to learn to give up whatever kept them from him —and follow him. So the paradox of our faith comes to completion. As has been said before, it is from darkness into light, from sorrow into joy, from losing to finding. And Jesus tells us not to be afraid.

I see my friend Kathleen smiling even as I write.

Elizabeth

4

EXPECTATIONS

In the early years of Kathleen's illness I must confess that I often had unreal expectations of my church. For many years I had served God's church and people as faithfully and diligently as I could. Surely, now, they would gather round and fall over each other in their anxiety to help us?

At first I felt hurt that so few of them did. Some excused themselves by asking, "What is the point in visiting? Kathleen may not recognise us! She may not remember us! It is all just a waste of time."

And I must confess that at first these excuses just angered me. Could they not understand that whether or not Kathleen recognised them was not really important? What she would recognise was the love and concern which they brought with them, and the sheer joy at seeing someone who obviously cared about her. But if they expected a response, then they would indeed be disappointed. A most beautiful smile and twinkling eyes, yes. But words? —this was no longer possible for her. And it was not her fault. Visitors who wanted conversation and vocal appreciation would need to go elsewhere. And they did. Visiting Kathleen was all too difficult.

Then one day I realised that my expectations were all too

27

unreal. Visiting someone with dementia was indeed extremely difficult. I thought back to my own visiting days in the parish, and had to admit that when I visited a parishioner I had expected and hoped for a response which would enable me to share information and greetings, and generally to get the person I was visiting to understand that my visit to them was not just a duty, but that I really did care about them and I wanted my visit to be of help to them.

But if there was no response, how could I continue? Somehow I did. But it was all so very difficult. And that I am sure is what my fellow Christians within the church were now feeling at the thought of visiting Kathleen. Could I blame them? To visit someone in hospital with a broken arm or leg was one thing. One could at least converse with them. But to visit someone with dementia who could neither respond nor converse? Well, that needed someone rather special, or someone with special training.

I also thought back to a course I had been sent on as a curate. It involved spending one day a week for several months at a local psychiatric hospital, working on the wards and talking to the patients. At the end of each day we, the participants, would meet together to share our experiences, and the leader would get us to write down, word for word, the conversations we had had with the patients. It was an amazing, enlightening experience. As I looked at my conversations, now written down for all my colleagues to see, I found myself asking questions of myself: Why had I said this or that? Why did I not pick up on what this or that patient had been trying to say to me, and encourage them further? Why was I so anxious to get away from the patients when the conversation became difficult? —or when I did not quite understand what they were trying to say to me? Was I not there to help them?

Each day we reviewed and discussed each other's experiences, and offered one other advice on what we felt should have happened. As a result we felt better able to face the next day with a new awareness of how best we could help people suffering from dementia. I like to think it worked. For me personally, it certainly made me listen more carefully to what patients were saying —even the ones who just seemed to be rambling on about nothing in particular, or who did not seem to care about whether I was there or not.

I now know that my presence did make a difference, as did the presence of other visitors. The stimulation alone was of immense value —and it was of this that I needed to be constantly reminded.

5

MOMENTS OF JOY

Yes, there have been many moments of joy —not least the realisation that at Glenside Manor Kathleen was with people who really cared about her and who made her happiness their main concern. I never cease to wonder at the patience and sheer dedication of the staff who work with – and struggle to help – those suffering from dementia. And yet this is what I now see for myself daily. And I am just so encouraged by what I see and hear.

This must, I feel, be due to the careful selection and the training of those who work with these very vulnerable people, and who are so clearly happy in their caring role. Their happiness is quite contagious, and obviously affects the residents, whose sheer contentment is apparent from the moment one steps into the nursing home.

When I am asked about how Kathleen copes with this kind of environment, I find that the best description I can give is that she is contented and gratefully accepts all that is being done for her. She eats well and drinks well and enjoys being taken out —not so easy in the winter months, but, with warm clothes, usually possible.

At the present moment my own mobility is a bit of a problem, and so although I can still – on a good day – push

Kathleen in a wheelchair around the grounds, there are days when I just have to accept my limitations and either just sit with her in her room and enjoy the privacy, whilst listening to some of her favourite music, or else take her for a drive to the river to feed the ducks. This she finds highly amusing. But she also finds something special in the peace and serenity of the riverside car park, so I know that such an outing will always be a success.

Occasionally, Elizabeth and I will take Kathleen out for coffee, lunch or afternoon tea, and this she really enjoys. The White Hart Hotel in Salisbury serves up some delicious sandwiches, which are quite a favourite with Kathleen, and we usually head for a special table in a corner by the log fire. It is a table from which she can see what is going on in the rest of the lounge, and that is usually of great interest to her.

Often she can pick up food such as sandwiches and cakes, and eat them in her own time. But drinking tea or coffee can be a bit hair-raising, especially if she is distracted, when the cup is inclined to tip alarmingly! Incredibly, if there are accidents with food or drinks she is oblivious to it all and just goes on smiling and enjoying her time out — which for me is such a blessing, for how awful it would be if such accidents distressed her and spoiled her time out with us. Once again it is the staff who are so kind and who brush aside our apologies for the mess with the assurance that it is no problem; tablecloths will wash, and vacuum cleaners are excellent for picking up food from the carpet!

"Does she still recognise you?" is a question which I am asked frequently by my friends and neighbours, and I have no hesitation in answering that she certainly does, and I think this is helped by the fact that I see her almost every day, and spend a lot of time with her. This is not always easy, because conversation is almost non-existent, and although browsing through magazines together does create some interest, that interest is gradually diminishing. Sadly, her interest in photographs, family or otherwise, is no longer as it was, and it is quite difficult to understand how many of these she recognises. Certainly her attention span is now quite short, and we can only spend a few moments on each picture before she looks away at other things in the room.

There were many happy days to follow the move to the nursing home: the days when we could go down to the river to feed the ducks; days when we could visit the local garden centre and admire the beautiful flowers and plants, always ending up in the coffee shop for tea or coffee and one of Kathleen's favourite ginger and apricot slices. Sometimes we would take a pretty plant back to put in her room. Always we would be treated with the utmost courtesy and kindness, all of which made us want to return another day. Anything that gave Kathleen pleasure and happiness was worth doing over and over again. So we did.

In the grounds of the nursing home were two miniature waterfalls cascading into a pond with water lilies. This was a favourite spot to visit and pause. We both loved it. The home had a talented and hard-working gardener who somehow made the whole of the grounds a pleasure to walk around and sit in. He was a remarkably cheerful character, who always had time to stop and pass the time of day. Kathleen, who by now was unable to converse, responded with one of her lovely smiles. Her conversation might well have been getting less and less, but her smiles more than made up for that.

Sunday worship had always been important to both of us and I was determined to maintain this as long as we possibly could. Distance made it impossible to continue worshipping in Alderbury, so we began attending the parish church at nearby Wilton, where they had a 10.30 a.m. Parish Eucharist every Sunday, with excellent music and a most welcoming congregation who took Kathleen to their hearts, and whose rector always greeted her with a hug.

By now Kathleen's mobility was becoming a problem, and we were advised to use a wheelchair as much as possible. Again the church responded with great alacrity. There was no need to bring a wheelchair from the nursing home. There was one already there. Not only that, but there were willing wardens and sidesmen who met us at the car and made light work of transferring her to and from the car, an operation which she found highly amusing —though I never quite understand why! My own inability to lift either Kathleen or the wheelchair could have made going to church impossible, but it was solved for us almost without asking.

So Sundays remained rather special for Kathleen. From the moment I call for her at the nursing home she is smiling or laughing, as if she knows exactly where we are going, and that it is somewhere she will enjoy. Once in the church, her wheelchair is placed alongside my pew so that we can hold hands and share the same books. For much of the service she quietly hums her own version of whatever the hymn is that is being sung. When it comes to the time of receiving communion there is usually some slight hesitation —but the patience and sensitivity of the minister always wins through, and she gratefully swallows both bread and wine. She may or may not understand what is happening.

Who knows? And does it matter? The One to whom it really matters knows.

Lots of kindnesses have been expressed in church. Often members of the congregation have gone out of their way, on their way back to their seats, to come across and give Kathleen a hug. Often she is unable to respond —but she clearly appreciates the gesture. One Mothering Sunday, when she was unable to go forward to receive a posy, someone came across and gave her theirs. She has always loved flowers, so this was a particularly great thing for that person to have done.

That our children, Gill and Jonathan, and her grand-children, are able to visit Kathleen frequently is also a source of great joy, as are the visits from close friends and those who have known her for some time. It has become increasingly clear to me that those who are relaxed, and who are fun to be with, are the ones Kathleen appreciates most, and she will often see the amusing side of some of the conversations that are going on around her. Whether she understands the joke is doubtful, but she laughs anyway, and we all laugh with her.

For her eightieth birthday we took her out to The Emblems restaurant for a celebration lunch, at which she tucked in and thoroughly enjoyed being the centre of attention and having all her family and friends around. It may well be that she did not understand the reason for the celebration, but she knew that it was special, and entered into the spirit of the occasion.

That was also the year of our golden wedding anniversary, and for this, anxious not to cause her too much stress, we divided our celebration into three separate occasions: a family lunch at The Emblems restaurant (it really is a favourite with Kath!); a tea party at home in Alderbury, and another tea party at Glenside Manor, with cake and champagne. That final event took place on the actual day of our wedding anniversary, so we arranged for Michael, our parish clergyman, to lead us, before tea, in the celebration of a special Eucharist, at which Kathleen and I were able to renew our marriage vows in the presence of our family and friends. It was all lovely and meaningful, and I was quite thrilled. Kathleen was radiant, just as she had been on our wedding day!

The discovery of wheelchair taxis was a real turning point in taking Kathleen out. Until then we had struggled to get her from wheelchair to car and then back again. It always needed at least two people, and there was always the risk that she would be hurt in the process. Once she slipped from our grasp, and we had to send for help to lift her from the ground. She was not hurt, but was unable to assist in any way, or even to take the weight on her own two feet. Logic is something which disappears during this illness, so that however bright and cheerful she appears, she cannot understand what is required of her or what it is we are asking.

These wheelchair taxi drivers are obviously trained to cope with people like Kathleen, and just take charge of the whole process, collecting her from inside the nursing home, pushing her gently up the ramp into the taxi, and then securing both her and the wheelchair for the journey, before ensuring that we, her carers, are also comfortable and secure. At our destination they make sure that we are safely in the church or restaurant before leaving. It was, we discovered, a great service, with kindly, helpful drivers, and we used it more and more until one day we found something even better: a vehicle of our own, with facilities similar to those in the wheelchair taxis.

The vehicle, which came to us as a gift, was a Renault Kangoo, and was fitted with a number of safety features. It had seats for three passengers as well as a wheelchair, and a shallow ramp at the rear which was neither too difficult nor too heavy for me to lift unaided.

Two of the straps which secured the wheelchair inside extended to allow the wheelchair to come down the ramp, but would not allow it to move away from the car. I was very impressed, and, after a trial run with Kathleen on board, decided that it was the best thing we had ever been shown and that it promised a great improvement in our caring for her. She, needless to say, was highly delighted and sat in her raised seat surveying all around her, beaming at all and sundry, and looking like a queen! I did not have to ask where was God in all this. It was clear!

Valentine's Day was another moment of great joy. We were able to lunch together, and I had managed to find a card which had little hearts all over it which started flashing when a certain place on the card was touched. This kept her amused for weeks! But I also received a beautiful Valentine's card 'from Kathleen'. What it is to have such thoughtful friends!

delight was every... when the pretty historic church came into view with its... ous countryside as a backdrop... We paused to look at the rural churchyard with our friends now buried there, in sure and certain hope of eternal life in God's presence.

6

MORE MOMENTS OF JOY

Elizabeth Burdett writes

Happiness might be a moment of ecstasy or an event in life
—perhaps a temporary one that takes one's breath away in
wonder and delight. Or it might be unsought, surprising
us with its intensity. But above all, happiness is fleeting.
Joy, on the other hand, is that beautiful fruit of the Spirit
which can express itself as contentment and peace, an inner
radiance that attracts others and encourages them to reflect
on its Source.

A bright and warm July day came as a joyful gift for
Kathleen as we drove together across Salisbury Plain in
response to an invitation she had received from the Mothers'
Union in Stanley's last parish before his retirement.

We spoke about our forthcoming visit during the journey
and the plans we had made to rediscover some familiar,
much-loved spots on our way to the 'Summer Lunch'.
Turning down the track to Rollestone church, Kathleen's
delight was obvious when the pretty, historic church came
into view, with glorious countryside as a backdrop. We
paused to look at the rural churchyard, remembering friends
now buried there 'in sure and certain hope of eternal life' in
God's presence.

Then on to the village itself and along to the Vicarage, where Stanley and Kathleen had spent sixteen years of joint ministry. Kathleen's pleasure was unmistakable as she pointed to the front door, the study window and, of course, the exquisite rose bush that never failed to bloom.

Reluctantly, we turned back and made our way to the Manor House and garden, where our hosts and many friends were waiting. My anxiety that so much excitement might be tiring Kathleen was short-lived. Smiling, kindly people surrounded the car, helping her into her wheelchair and finding a quiet, shady place in the garden for her to share with so many friends. They came in turn to speak with her, bringing a delicious summer lunch and then taking her for a walk around the beautiful garden. Then, as midday prayers filled the air, 'our Kath' joined quietly in the Lord's Prayer. Joy indeed, in the deepest sense of the word. But the best was yet to come. Tiredness was becoming apparent, so we returned to the car for the journey home, making our way down the long drive to the gate. As we approached it we were astonished to see that each side of the path was lined with Kathleen's friends, smiling, waving arms and scarves, as they sang their farewells. We returned home with full hearts —full of thanksgiving and joy for the gifts of love and friendship given to Kathleen that day by God who treasures and loves her.

As she fell asleep by my side I pondered on the feelings of heartache and loss during the early days of her diagnosis, and how fears of sadness can become songs of joy. The words of Psalm 4:7f came to mind:

> You have filled my heart with greater joy,
> than when their grain and new wine abound.

I will lie down and sleep in peace,
for you alone, O LORD,
make me dwell in safety.

Arriving home after a busy day, did Kath understand the prayer we shared with clasped hands? I do not know. But her smiling eyes were enough. I prayed that God would lighten our way, that his joy would dwell within us; that we might be confident of his love —safe, and certain that we were in his keeping.

Elizabeth

WANDERING

... one that involved punishment was left alone with dementia.

... while her ... and became that more ... she had ... after he desired ... the ability to walk around and needed ... much in wheelchair or assistance from members of staff. This also meant that I was unable to take her to walk around the grounds, and that a wheelchair became more

7

WANDERING

In one of my earlier parishes we had a lady with dementia who would don her nightclothes and head off towards the nearby town, convinced that she was on her way back to see her parents in Wales, and that they would be waiting for her. She could not let them down and needed to go at once. She usually managed to slip away from the house without anyone seeing her, and it was not until she was picked up by the police some hours later, often freezing cold, that anyone was aware that she was missing.

Wandering is a very common trait in people with dementia, yet in Kathleen's case it was limited to wandering around the nursing home, sometimes going in and out of people's rooms just to 'tidy up'. No one minded, and she was quite easy to find if needed. The outer doors were kept locked, so there was no danger of her wandering off and getting lost, or straying on to the main road where the traffic was an obvious hazard.

As she grew older and became rather more frail, she had neither the desire nor the ability to walk around, and needed either a wheelchair or assistance from members of staff. This also meant that I was unable to take her for walks around the grounds, and that a wheelchair became more and more a necessity. But even with a wheelchair we were able to stop and enjoy the miniature waterfalls and lily pond, and to sit on a garden seat and gaze across the valley. Often Kathleen would try to talk to me, but because the words were all rather muddled it was difficult to make sense of what she was trying to say. But I tried hard to give a reasonable response, and we often ended up by having a good laugh together. Those were very special moments indeed.

Our son, Jonathan, sometimes refers to the day when he was visiting her and suddenly, without warning, she just got up and wandered off around the home. Did she get tired of us, he mused?

On other occasions our daughter, Gill, would be trying unsuccessfully to attract her attention when, after about an hour, Kathleen would look up with a surprised expression and say, "Oh hello" – as though she had only just noticed that Gill was there. But all these were things to which we became accustomed, and were usually followed up by a lovely smile which more than made up for everything else.

8

AT THE BREAKING OF BREAD

Elizabeth Burdett writes

A bright October day – of golden, autumnal sunshine, falling leaves and a sparkle in the air – hinted that the end of another summer was near. It was a perfect start for the day that Stanley had planned to spend with Kathleen at a favourite place of theirs, Friars Cliff at Mudeford, near Christchurch. A breath of sea air, and lunch at a nearby hotel, would be a pleasant way for Kathleen and Stanley to be together. I was pleased and proud to be included.

We left Salisbury in good spirits, having picked up Kathleen at Glenside Manor. She entertained both driver and passenger with sweet song as we journeyed through Ringwood and Fordingbridge to our destination.

Mudeford is a delightful corner of Bournemouth Bay, with an atmosphere of old world charm —a combination of fishing harbour, sailing boats and, just around the corner, a pretty, tree-lined walk, with the sight and sound of the sea through the trees, and the Isle of Wight outlined in the warm sunshine. So a stroll along to the harbour entrance gave us a lovely view of where the River Avon, having passed through our home town of Salisbury, is united with the sea at 'The Run'.

A sense of timelessness filled the air as we found a sheltered spot and a welcome seat from which to view the many interesting things around: Christchurch Priory in the distance, Hengistbury Head, and the hotel where we were to enjoy lunch.

Kathleen smiled with pleasure as she sat beside her dear Stanley (on the seat specially made for them, of course!) savouring all the joys of being beside the sea.

Time for lunch, though, and a short drive to a hotel, so long appreciated by us all for its amazing position and welcoming staff. We were shown to our table in the attractive restaurant, but suddenly our smiling, happy Kathleen became withdrawn and uncommunicative, showing little interest in the meal that Stanley had ordered for her. Perhaps the day's excitement had proved too much for her, we thought – perhaps, maybe – we shall never know, but we whispered our thanksgiving in the 'grace before meals', and waited. For it was the moment when her priestly husband took bread, broke it, and gave it to her, that Kathleen visibly relaxed, took the bread, smiled at Stanley and enjoyed the remainder of the meal with her usual appreciation.

For Christians every meal is a sacramental meal, taken within the presence of our living Lord as host and guest. And this meal was certainly no exception.

Elizabeth

9

FAMILY

Reflections from daughter, Gill

It does seem a long time ago now, but I think my first reaction was one of disbelief. I thought that it was stress, and that this explained what I perceived as odd behaviour —keys going missing, being very late, driving too fast and thinking that this was fine, not wanting to be seen walking to church dressed up.

I went through the stage of blaming God. I felt that it was very unfair —my parents had given so much, so why couldn't they have a happy retirement?

I have been shocked at the lack of understanding and support from the church and Christian people. With one or two exceptions, and except for Wilton Church, they have not wanted to know. As a Christian who does not particularly enjoy church life, it has added fuel to a fire. I think that the majority of Christians would be ashamed if they were aware of the understanding, care and support that Mum and Dad have received from non-Christians. For a time I used this as a very good reason not to go to church and to criticise Christians, but I have mellowed over the years.

As I have heard other stories of people with Alzheimer's,

I have realised that God has looked after my parents —they are in the best place with the best care. Salisbury Alzheimer's Society were great, and now Glenside is one of the best places that Mum could be. The people there really care and do their very best, the facilities are nice and rooms are aired, etc, every day.

It has been sad to see Mum change over the years and become less and less aware of me and my life. There was a time when it was embarrassing, when she would point and laugh at fat people (which is so unlike the real person she was), but not now that she is less aware. Sometimes I forget the person she was —looking through old photos brings back some of the memories. She always sat on the floor, the arm of a chair or a footstool. I would like to remember her as she was then. She was a good cook, academically intelligent, always wanted to look after us (and my horse, even though she wasn't really used to them) rather than as she is now.

I now want to go and see her on the basis that she might enjoy the visit even if she cannot communicate it. Like everyone, my time is often short and it is disappointing if she doesn't wake up or won't acknowledge me, but that is part of it and I have grown to accept it and am quite used to it. I would have liked her to see my new flat, and get to know the man in my life (she has met him, though she would not have known who it was), and so on.

I hope that she will continue to be happy in herself —I have heard stories of people who were clearly unhappy.

Living with dementia —reflections by son, Jonathan

My reaction when I first heard that Mum had been diagnosed as having Alzheimer's disease was a mixture of shock, sadness, disappointment and worry about how she would cope —and how Dad would cope with looking after her. There was uncertainty too, for we did not know how bad it would get, nor how quickly.

Then there was the thought of how unfair this was, just as Dad was approaching retirement, with plans about all the things they would now be able to do together and all the time they would have to relax together after a pretty busy working life. Instead of that, Dad's time would now be spent looking after Mum.

I well remember the first signs of Mum's illness— forgetfulness, putting things in strange places, and often repeating sentences over and over again. Initially it could be frustrating, to be asked the same question a number of times, particularly before her diagnosis. Even after the diagnosis it could still be frustrating, but we all had to learn to be tolerant and to remember that it was not her fault.

I sometimes found that it was worth taking the lighter approach. Rather than getting annoyed when asked the same question yet again, I would give a different answer each time, giving me more to think about, and knowing that it did not matter too much, since she would quickly forget what I had told her!

How did all this affect our lives? Well, in the early stages Dad's life was affected greatly, but ours – since we did not live with her – were not really affected on a daily basis. But if there was a function of any kind we had to consider how she would be affected or react, and whether it was really a good idea to take her.

More recently we have become used to it, but feel a great sadness that we can no longer have a conversation with her, and have no idea how much she has taken in.

And what of her grandchildren? Well Ben, Zac and Zoë did not know Mum before her illness, and so they just became used to her the way she is. They have never really questioned as to what is wrong with her, but they do find it increasingly unsettling when we go to visit her, especially as they are now getting older. Seeing the other nursing home residents with their various conditions can also worry them a little.

All this means that they will probably want to visit less as they get older. One of my regrets is that Mum did not get to know her grandchildren properly. How lovely it would have been for Ben, Zac and Zoë to have known their grandmother as she used to be.

And now? Well the thought I often have (selfishly) is, "I just hope it never happens to me." How can this dreadful disease be prevented? What tests can be done? Is it in the genes? Because Mum has it, will I get it? Will any of my children get it? Questions to which we at present have no answers.

10

COMMUNICATION

One of the most distressing and frustrating things which happens to a person with dementia is their inability to communicate in the same way as they have always done. I sometimes watch, feeling rather helpless, as Kathleen struggles to formulate words, as she longs to express something which is on her mind. Having uttered some garbled sounds she will then look at me in anticipation of a response which, all too often, I find impossible to provide since I have not understood a word of what she was trying to say.

Having come to understand the importance of encouraging her, I do some guesswork and respond as best as I am able, and hope that that will be acceptable. Usually it is, though I long to know what she was really trying to say to me. Occasionally she will utter a phrase or a sentence with absolute clarity and that, for me, is very exciting. But that does not happen very often, and when it does I have to pick it up very quickly, for it will not be repeated!

Singing, too, is something which she still enjoys and she will often, quite unprompted, burst into song. The fact that both the music and the words are being made up as she goes along does not matter one bit. The thing is that she enjoys her singing and is clearly very happy doing so. This may be due to the fact that for many years she sang (and sang well) in church choirs, operatic societies and choral societies, and loved both the music and the friendships which were a part of these activities.

Music is generally regarded as therapeutic, and with this in mind I bought her a radio/CD player for her room. This means that we can now spend many an hour there, listening to a variety of music, and sometimes beating time to some of the more lively pieces. Not surprisingly, hymn tunes are among her favourites and so we have quite a collection of those.

Before she became ill she enjoyed playing the piano, but needed more and more help with this as the illness progressed. We were very pleased to discover an excellent piano teacher who fully understood Kathleen's problem and who was sensitive and kind enough to encourage her without making her feel useless, and for this I shall always be grateful. Sadly, this music teacher moved away and we were unable to get a replacement. I tried to encourage her myself by playing simple duets, and we had lots of fun doing this, but she really needed more professional help, and because this was not available her interest gradually waned.

We still have the Broadwood baby grand of which Kathleen was very proud, and, although I would never sell it, it rarely gets used these days. To sell it now would be rather like getting rid of a part of my dear wife. Instead it provides an excellent place on which to display family photographs, and for our tiny grandchildren to amuse themselves as they pretend to be great pianists whilst making as much noise as possible!

Recently we had a family tea party at home to celebrate Mothering Sunday, and whilst gifts and flowers were exchanged on arrival, it soon became clear that the effort required to communicate with Kathleen after that was just too much, and so she became more or less an observer. This comment is not meant as criticism because, as one who visits her most days of the week, I fully understand the difficulty of trying to get a response. Yet how does one maintain a relationship without communication? I am constantly aware of the importance of developing further gifts of listening, encouragement and interpretation, and not arriving too quickly at the point of assuming that 'nothing more can be done' —a point reached all too often and too quickly by some of my church colleagues.

11

LIFE WITHOUT KATHLEEN

January? It can't possibly be! A day of brilliant sunshine with mild temperatures, and yet my diary confirms that it is in fact 23rd January. And I am certainly making the most of it, having been treated to a two-day break at the Carlton Hotel in Bournemouth.

I came here a couple of years ago with Kath, and well remember the sheer luxury of the hotel and the delectable menus, to say nothing of the lovely indoor swimming pool and comfortable lounges. Sadly, even if she were able to be with me this week, the relentless Alzheimer's disease would prevent her from appreciating all the many aspects of this place which meant so much to both of us just that short time ago. Indeed, to uproot her from her now familiar surroundings at the nursing home would, I know, just confuse and unsettle her.

So here I am on my own. I don't like it. But it does give me a break without upsetting Kath. And I must confess that I did feel in need of one.

I try hard to be sensible as I begin to have regrets about leaving her behind. I think of all the good breaks and holidays we have had together over the years, and nothing will ever take away the sheer joy of sharing so much in so many beautiful places. We have indeed been blessed, and I know that it is time now to stop looking backwards and to look ahead to whatever the Master himself has planned for us.

In the meantime I never cease to be amazed at his wonderful timing. When I fell off the ladder, God knew that I was getting past caring for Kathleen twenty-four hours a day, and whilst I do not believe that he created the accident, I do know that he used it to ensure that Kath was given the kind of professional help and care which she both needed and deserved. That she accepted it without a murmur, which really helped on her way forward, was something for which I shall always be thankful.

Yes, indeed I would have continued looking after her at home, but it somehow needed my accident to show me that it was not in anyone's interest for me to do that —least of all in Kath's. I do love her more than ever, and I want only the best for her 'till death us do part'.

12

THE ALZHEIMER'S SOCIETY

I was first introduced to the Alzheimer's Society by the consultant who was responsible for Kath's diagnosis, and was immediately impressed by the genuine kindness and caring of those we met. We were fed with lots of information on how to cope and where to get help, none of which sounded particularly relevant to us at that time, since Kathleen was still in the early stages of dementia, and we had not been faced with many of the real problems of living with the disease. Those were to come.

Soon after that, I was away for a few days at St Joseph's House of Prayer, and was somehow prompted to listen to a tape about Alzheimer's disease by someone I was later to discover was a key figure in a branch of the Alzheimer's Society. What she had to say was in fact quite depressing, as it seemed to offer little or no hope of a recovery but spoke in quite stark terms of the various stages of the disease through which we would have to live.

Tears welled up inside me as I thought of Kathleen being robbed of so much that was good in life, and of so many things which she had enjoyed to the full. I stopped crying, only to offer up the whole situation in prayer. And then I felt better. After all, if there was a God then surely he could cope with this far better than I could. So I decided I could leave it safely in his hands And I did.

Back home, the local branch of the Alzheimer's Society had already swung into action, and I was invited to take Kathleen along to a Day Club once or twice a week, where we were both made very welcome. These visits were not always enjoyed by Kathleen, who felt that she was being 'talked down to' and was not able to understand just why she was there at all. In the end I had to concede defeat and we stopped going.

We did, however, continue to attend many of the social events, talks and discussions, and found these very helpful indeed. I was always amazed at the dedication of the volunteers who organised these events, and determined that one day I too would become such a volunteer.

The Alzheimer's Society is a great organisation, which we have found extremely helpful in all kinds of ways. One of the things which I quickly discovered through my contact with other sufferers was that, just as each healthy person is quite different from the next, so it is that sufferers from Alzheimer's disease are also all different from each other, and seem to suffer in different ways. One cannot therefore make blanket assertions because the illness develops a path specific to each individual, and no two people's dementia is the same.

It follows, then, that the care and treatment of individuals will also need to vary from person to person, and this is one of the things which impressed me about the care given at Glenside Manor. The individual tastes and needs were quickly recognised, even when verbal communication was almost nonexistent, and the residents were made to feel that they mattered and that the meeting of their needs was as important to the staff as it was to the residents themselves.

It also became apparent to me that, even when residents were being perhaps rather difficult, they were dealt with kindly, gently and sensitively, and every effort was made to reason with them even when 'reason' seemed impossible to achieve. Visitors were (and are) always made to feel welcome, usually being greeted with tea or coffee. If privacy is required, then this is also made possible.

Never have we been made to feel a nuisance or unwelcome, and however busy they are, they always have time to listen to our concerns or requests, and we are made to feel that we really matter, too. Having heard and read about the indifferent attitudes of staff in some nursing homes, I have always been so grateful, and given thanks for the fact that Kathleen is where she is. We are just so blessed.

13

LIFE BEYOND THE ILLNESS

One of the many things for which I know I have to be
thankful is that Kathleen has not succumbed to the kind
of aggressive behaviour which is so common in many
sufferers. And this would seem to be because no two
people have the same personality, the same history or the
same pattern of health. Each one of us is unique, thanks
to our wonderful Creator God. And each one of us reacts
differently to the blows which life has dealt us.

But whilst I cannot overstate my regret that my dear wife
is suffering from this terrible disease, I am also fully aware
of the wonderful ways in which God is using the illness
(and us) to bring us closer to him, showing us new ways of
living this earthly life positively.

Some days when I visit Kathleen, she is tired and sleepy
and curled up in a chair with her eyes closed. The temptation
is to rouse her and say, "Hey look, I'm here," in the hope
that she would be motivated to sit up and spend some
quality time with me. And then I realise that she is really
enjoying a most wonderful deep peace, which is probably
doing her far more good than my idle chatter! And so I let
her be. If she wakes up while I am still there, then that is a
bonus, but I would be doing her no real favour by rudely

awakening her, even if there is a cup of tea in front of her gradually getting cold! And that peace is a peace which I begin to feel myself as I sit by her side and look across at her relaxed expression. That, perhaps, is my reward. I reflect on how she seems to get tired much more quickly these days, and am advised by the staff that this is because the brain now has to work so much harder in order to keep up.

I have read that people with dementia become unable to deal with complex issues because 'there is less storage space for ideas', and that they often become more self-centred, because it now requires much more effort to think about the needs of anyone else. And yet this is the reverse of my experience with Kathleen, who is just as courteous and thoughtful now as she has ever been, though expressing these feelings is often, for her, quite difficult. She will sometimes try, and will then lapse into silence as the whole effort becomes impossible.

Living with Kathleen's dementia has taught us so much about this condition, and about those who are affected by it. But perhaps the most important thing I have learnt is that it is just an illness: a terrible illness, yes; a life-changing illness, yes. But, as I journey through these closing years of Kathleen's life, I am being made aware that the real Kathleen shines through the dementia with her natural charm and gracious behaviour.

Over and over again I am able to see and hold close the Kathleen I have known and loved so much for so many years, and, despite the illness, I can feel that she is still the same loving wife and sweetheart. Her unique individuality has not been lost in the clinical condition which is now beyond her control. Those baffling moments when I cannot understand what Kathleen is saying or to whom she is referring can often be dispelled by a laugh or a joke, and it is then that I realise that there is indeed a great deal of life to be lived beyond the illness.

Postscript: 'Prelude to Joy'
Elizabeth Burdett writes

What has Kathleen's ten-year journey of ongoing illness meant to her and to those who love and care for her? It would be presumptuous to speak for her or her family, but there are certainly many positives along the way, the greatest of all being the strength, gentleness and humour that flow from Kathleen. She radiates inner peace and joy, especially when worshipping with her dearly loved husband. She can no longer speak very well, but she sings beautifully, reminding us of her years in the church choir. And Stanley's devotion and constant visits are an added pleasure, particularly when they include a lunchtime meal or afternoon tea.

These loving times of encouragement and hope are part of the pilgrimage, but of course there are also times of frustration and pain for Kathleen and her loved ones. God's presence and power are revealed through human weakness in a very special way— the still small voice of comfort when courage fails; the love that is expressed through the gift of family and friends; the beauty of each new day.

Every family has its own story of heartache and difficulty to tell, and there are often no easy answers and no clear way forward, but for as long as love remains and hope strengthens the human heart, we know in our inmost self that this is indeed the prelude to joy.